Book Design by Gabrielle Fitzpatrick

ISBN 978-1-7353211-0-3

Published by Be Who You Needed Enterprises, LLC

# Introduction *To Your Journal*

Learning how to manage my symptoms associated with Bipolar Disorder required patience and discipline. As I tried different treatments, one thing that stood out to me was the need to learn who I was in all facets of life. I needed to establish my triggers, my protective factors, and my patterns.

We often get so ingrained in our journey that much of it becomes automatic, and we forget how things contribute to or hinder our mental wellness. This journal will take you on a journey of internally tuning in to you and will allow you to recognize factors in your life that require your attention to change. You will learn to be mindful of what you consume with things such as food, people, TV, and social media as well as how your consumption levels affect your mood and feelings.

As you discover yourself, you will need to be as transparent and honest as possible when completing your entries. This is your journal designed for your self-improvement. Don't hold back. If you need help identifying your feelings, there is a feelings and emotions list for your reference.

There is beauty in learning more about yourself and making your mental well-being a priority. Search within, reflect, and discover you.

Rwenshaun L. Miller, LCMHC, NCC

**Utilize this tool to compliment therapy, and if you are noticing that you are constantly having thoughts of harming yourself or harming others, please visit your local behavioral health center or contact the National Suicide Prevention Lifeline at 1-800-273-8255.**

| Sunday | Monday | Tuesday |
|--------|--------|---------|
|        |        |         |
|        |        |         |
|        |        |         |
|        |        |         |
|        |        |         |

MONTH: _____

| Wednesday | Thursday | Friday | Saturday |
|-----------|----------|--------|----------|
| | | | |
| | | | |
| | | | |
| | | | |
| | | | |

|  | 1 | 2 | 3 | 4 | 5 | 6 |
|---|---|---|---|---|---|---|
| **Key Tasks** |  | ✓ |  | ✓ |  | ✓ |
| Example: Workout |  |  |  |  |  |  |
| - - - - - - - - - - - - - - - - - - - - |  |  |  |  |  |  |
| - - - - - - - - - - - - - - - - - - - - |  |  |  |  |  |  |
| - - - - - - - - - - - - - - - - - - - - |  |  |  |  |  |  |
| - - - - - - - - - - - - - - - - - - - - |  |  |  |  |  |  |
| - - - - - - - - - - - - - - - - - - - - |  |  |  |  |  |  |
| - - - - - - - - - - - - - - - - - - - - |  |  |  |  |  |  |
| - - - - - - - - - - - - - - - - - - - - |  |  |  |  |  |  |
| - - - - - - - - - - - - - - - - - - - - |  |  |  |  |  |  |
| - - - - - - - - - - - - - - - - - - - - |  |  |  |  |  |  |
| - - - - - - - - - - - - - - - - - - - - |  |  |  |  |  |  |

- - - - - - - - - - - - - - - - - - - -

√        √    √    √        √

## Key Tasks

--------------------------------

--------------------------------

--------------------------------

--------------------------------

--------------------------------

--------------------------------

--------------------------------

--------------------------------

--------------------------------

--------------------------------

--------------------------------

--------------------------------

# FEELINGS AND EMOTIONS WORDS LIST

## A

Angry, Annoyed, Afraid, Awkward, Affectionate, Anxious, Alarmed, Awed, Aggravated, Amazed, Astonished, Amused, Apprehensive, Absorbed, Ambivalent, Ashamed, Able, Addled, Admired, Admirable, Affable, Agreeable, Aggressive, Abandoned

## B

Brave, Bothered, Bewildered, Bitter, Bashful, Blue, Baffled, Blissful, Buoyant, Bereaved, Bold

## C

Cheerful, Cooperative, Confident, Calm, Cold, Curious, Content, Considerate, Cautious, Cranky, Crestfallen, Contrite, Chagrined, Carefree, Composed, Capable, Caring, Careful, Contemptuous, Cross, Concerned, Complacent, Charitable, Crushed, Cantankerous, Compulsive

## D

Defiant, Depressed, Discouraged, Delighted, Disgusted, Determined, Disappointed, Detached, Daring, Disillusioned, Devious, Dismayed, Disenchanted, Doleful, Disinterested, Disdainful, Dismissive, Dejected, Disengaged, Distant

## E

Elated, Enthusiastic, Embarrassed, Edgy, Excited, Envious, Exhausted, Eager, Exuberant, Enraged, Euphoric, Extravagant, Ecstatic, Eager, Emboldened

## F

Funny, Frightened, Fearful, Furious, Fair, Foolish, Frustrated, Forgiving, Flustered, Fulfilled, Fatigued

## G

Grouchy, Guilty, Grief-stricken, Generous, Greedy, Grateful, Grumpy, Guarded, Gleeful, Glad, Gloomy, Glum, Gracious, Grateful

## H

Happy, Humiliated, Hurt, Helpless, Hopeless, Horrified, Hesitant, Humbled, Heartbroken, Hysterical, Hyperactive

## I

Irritated, Irritable, Interested, Insecure, Impatient, Inspired, Inspiring, Inadequate, Irrational, Ignorant, Indifferent, Irked, Impertinent, Inquisitive, Isolated

## J

Jealous, Joyful, Joyous, Judgmental, Judged, Jaded, Jocular, Jittery

## K

Kind, Keen

## L

Loving, Lonely, Lackluster, Leery, Lethargic, Listless, Lazy

## M

Mad, Meek, Mean, Miserable, Malevolent, Marvelous, Manipulated, Manipulative, Misunderstood, Mischievous, Mopey, Melodramatic, Moody, Melancholy, Mirthful, Moved, Morose, Manic

## N

Nice, Naughty, Nasty, Nervous, Neglected, Neglectful, Needy, Needed, Naive, Nonchalant, Nonplussed, Numb

## O

Overpowered, Overjoyed, Obedient, Obsessive, Obsessed, Offended, Outraged, Overloaded, Overstimulated, Obstinate, Obligated, Optimistic, Open, Open-minded

## P

Panicked, Panicky, Peaceful, Placid, Playful, Pensive, Puzzled, Powerful, Powerless, Pleased, Petty, Petulant, Preoccupied, Proud, Prideful, Prickly, Petrified, Pressured, Perturbed, Peeved, Passive

## Q

Quirky, Quarrelsome, Qualified, Quivery, Querulous, Quiet

## R

Relieved, Relaxed, Resentful, Rattled, Refreshed, Repulsed, Rational, Reasonable, Reasoned, Rebellious, Reluctant, Reassured, Remorseful, Reserved, Rejuvenated, Restless, Rattled

## S

Sad, Surprised, Silly, Scared, Sorrowful, Serious, Shy, Satisfied, Sensitive, Safe, Stressed, Stubborn, Sarcastic, Spiteful, Scornful, Secure, Serene, Smug, Sociable, Sympathetic, Startled, Satisfied, Sanguine, Skeptical, Sincere

## T

Thankful, Tearful, Teary, Thoughtful, Tolerant, Tolerated, Trusted, Trusting, Trustworthy, Temperamental, Terrified, Timid, Tired, Tiresome, Troubled, Tickled, Torn, Touched, Threatened, Tender, Tranquil

## U

Uneasy, Uncertain, Uncomfortable, Unruffled, Unafraid, Useless, Useful, Unimpressed, Unappreciated, Undecided, Unruly, Uptight, Unnerved, Unhappy, Unsteady, Uplifted, Unsure

## V

Vivacious, Vain, Vibrant, Violent, Valued, Valuable, Vital, Vexed, Volatile, Vulnerable, Victorious, Victimized, Vacant

## W

Worried, Wary, Weak, Weary, Wistful, Wishful, Willful, Willing, Woeful, Weepy, Whiny, Worn, Whimsical, Warm, Witty, Withdrawn, Worthless, Wronged, Wasted, Worldly

## Y

Youthful, Yielding, Yearning

## Z

Zany, Zealous, Zestful

**We experience more feelings and emotions than happy/sad, mad/glad or good/bad. We are not always given the tools (words) to communicate how we truly feel, so here's a list to assist with your accuracy. Use these words to document how you feel on a daily in your journal.**

## HEALTH & WELLNESS

### FOOD

**BREAKFAST:**
Oatmeal, Fruit

**LUNCH:**
Baked Chicken, Spinach

**DINNER:**
Salmon, Sweet Potato, Spinach

**SNACK (IF ANY):**
Peanuts, Fruit

**WATER INTAKE**

### EXERCISE

(Description)  Chest + Biceps

TIME: 5:00 am     QUALITY: $\frac{7}{10}$     HRS: 45 mins

### OTHER

HRS OF TV, COMPUTER, PHONE:
1hr TV, 9 hrs Computer, 4hrs Phone

MEDS:                          ALCOHOL/DRUGS:
Vitamins                       None

## HOW DID YOU SLEEP?

HRS OF SLEEP: 5.5     QUALITY OF SLEEP: ① ② ③ ④ ⑤̸ ⑥ ⑦ ⑧ ⑨ ⑩

## HOW DID I MAKE MYSELF A PRIORITY TODAY?

I read a book for leisure

## LET'S TALK ABOUT IT. TODAY I AM...

**GRATEFUL FOR:**

Food to eat. Talking to pops. Help from my classmate.

**FEELING (WHY? USE FEELING WORDS FROM LIST):**

O  Discouraged (bad grade in class)          O  Elated (off work today)

O  Irritable (limited sleep)                       O

**TALKED TO** (HOW DID I FEEL AFTER?):

Cousin (Annoyed), Boss (Angry)

**LISTENING TO:**

90's R&B

**READING:**

## TODAY'S REFLECTION

(EUSTRESSIN' OR YOU STRESSIN?)

Today I got my grade from my test, and I didn't do well. The semester is

almost over, and I don't know if I will pass.

## WHAT GOOD THINGS HAPPENED TODAY?

My mom sent some money

Had a good conversation with a stranger in the gym

## NOTE TO SELF...

If I could do anything different, I would...

I will take time for a nap

## Important Dates

PLANNING FOR:
---------------------------------------------------------------

UPCOMING EVENTS:
---------------------------------------------------------------

LOOKING FORWARD TO:
---------------------------------------------------------------

## Top Priorities

- ---------------------------------------------------------------
- ---------------------------------------------------------------
- ---------------------------------------------------------------
- ---------------------------------------------------------------
- ---------------------------------------------------------------
- ---------------------------------------------------------------
- ---------------------------------------------------------------

# THIS MONTH *I Will...*

CHALLENGE MYSELF TO:

- _____

IMPROVE ON:

- _____

STRIVE FOR:

- _____

WORK TOWARDS:

- _____

## MONTHLY *goals*

## HEALTH & WELLNESS

FOOD

BREAKFAST:
_____

LUNCH:
_____

DINNER:
_____

SNACK (IF ANY):
_____

WATER INTAKE ▯▯▯▯▯▯▯▯

EXERCISE

(Description) _____

TIME:          QUALITY:          HRS:

OTHER

HRS OF TV, COMPUTER, PHONE:
_____

MEDS:                    ALCOHOL/DRUGS:
_____        _____

## HOW DID YOU SLEEP?

🕐 HRS OF SLEEP: _____     QUALITY OF SLEEP: ① ② ③ ④ ⑤ ⑥ ⑦ ⑧ ⑨ ⑩

HOW DID I MAKE MYSELF A PRIORITY TODAY?

-------------------------------------------------------------

## LET'S TALK ABOUT IT.  TODAY I AM...

**GRATEFUL FOR:**

-------------------------------------------------------------

**FEELING (WHY? USE FEELING WORDS FROM LIST):**

○                                              ○

○                                              ○

**TALKED TO** (HOW DID I FEEL AFTER?):

-------------------------------------------------------------

**LISTENING TO:**

-------------------------------------------------------------

**READING:**

-------------------------------------------------------------

## TODAY'S REFLECTION
(EUSTRESSIN' OR YOU STRESSIN?)

---

## WHAT GOOD THINGS HAPPENED TODAY?

---

## NOTE TO SELF...
If I could do anything different, I would...

---

## HEALTH & WELLNESS

FOOD

BREAKFAST:

LUNCH:

DINNER:

SNACK (IF ANY):

WATER INTAKE

EXERCISE

(Description) _____

TIME:          QUALITY:          HRS:

OTHER

HRS OF TV, COMPUTER, PHONE:

MEDS:                    ALCOHOL/DRUGS:

## HOW DID YOU SLEEP?

🕐 HRS OF SLEEP: _____     QUALITY OF SLEEP: ① ② ③ ④ ⑤ ⑥ ⑦ ⑧ ⑨ ⑩

HOW DID I MAKE MYSELF A PRIORITY TODAY?

---

## LET'S TALK ABOUT IT.  TODAY I AM...

**GRATEFUL FOR:**

---

**FEELING (WHY? USE FEELING WORDS FROM LIST):**

○                                    ○

○                                    ○

**TALKED TO** (HOW DID I FEEL AFTER?):

---

**LISTENING TO:**

---

**READING:**

---

19

## TODAY'S REFLECTION
(EUSTRESSIN' OR YOU STRESSIN?)

-------------------------------------------------------------------

-------------------------------------------------------------------

-------------------------------------------------------------------

-------------------------------------------------------------------

-------------------------------------------------------------------

-------------------------------------------------------------------

-------------------------------------------------------------------

-------------------------------------------------------------------

-------------------------------------------------------------------

-------------------------------------------------------------------

## WHAT GOOD THINGS HAPPENED TODAY?

-------------------------------------------------------------------

-------------------------------------------------------------------

-------------------------------------------------------------------

## NOTE TO SELF...
If I could do anything different, I would...

-------------------------------------------------------------------

-------------------------------------------------------------------

-------------------------------------------------------------------

-------------------------------------------------------------------

## HEALTH & WELLNESS

FOOD

🍵 BREAKFAST:

🥤 LUNCH:

🍽 DINNER:

⬜ SNACK (IF ANY):

WATER INTAKE 🥤🥤🥤🥤🥤🥤🥤🥤

EXERCISE

(Description) _____

TIME:          QUALITY:          HRS:

**OTHER**

📺 HRS OF TV, COMPUTER, PHONE:

MEDS:                    ALCOHOL/DRUGS:

## HOW DID YOU SLEEP?

🕐 HRS OF SLEEP: _____     **QUALITY OF SLEEP:** ① ② ③ ④ ⑤ ⑥ ⑦ ⑧ ⑨ ⑩

HOW DID I MAKE MYSELF A PRIORITY TODAY?

-------------------------------------------------------------------

## LET'S TALK ABOUT IT.  TODAY I AM...

**GRATEFUL FOR:**

-------------------------------------------------------------------

**FEELING (WHY? USE FEELING WORDS FROM LIST):**

○                                   ○

○                                   ○

**TALKED TO** (HOW DID I FEEL AFTER?):

-------------------------------------------------------------------

**LISTENING TO:**

-------------------------------------------------------------------

**READING:**

-------------------------------------------------------------------

## TODAY'S REFLECTION
(EUSTRESSIN' OR YOU STRESSIN?)

------------------------------------------------------------

------------------------------------------------------------

------------------------------------------------------------

------------------------------------------------------------

------------------------------------------------------------

------------------------------------------------------------

------------------------------------------------------------

------------------------------------------------------------

------------------------------------------------------------

## WHAT GOOD THINGS HAPPENED TODAY?

------------------------------------------------------------

------------------------------------------------------------

------------------------------------------------------------

## NOTE TO SELF...
If I could do anything different, I would...

------------------------------------------------------------

------------------------------------------------------------

------------------------------------------------------------

------------------------------------------------------------

## HEALTH & WELLNESS

FOOD

BREAKFAST:

LUNCH:

DINNER:

SNACK (IF ANY):

WATER INTAKE

EXERCISE

(Description) _____

TIME:          QUALITY:          HRS:

OTHER

HRS OF TV, COMPUTER, PHONE:

MEDS:                    ALCOHOL/DRUGS:

## HOW DID YOU SLEEP?

HRS OF SLEEP: _____     QUALITY OF SLEEP: ① ② ③ ④ ⑤ ⑥ ⑦ ⑧ ⑨ ⑩

HOW DID I MAKE MYSELF A PRIORITY TODAY?

--------------------------------------------

## LET'S TALK ABOUT IT.  TODAY I AM...

**GRATEFUL FOR:**

--------------------------------------------

**FEELING (WHY? USE FEELING WORDS FROM LIST):**

○                              ○

○                              ○

**TALKED TO** (HOW DID I FEEL AFTER?):

--------------------------------------------

**LISTENING TO:**

--------------------------------------------

**READING:**

--------------------------------------------

## TODAY'S REFLECTION

(EUSTRESSIN' OR YOU STRESSIN?)

------------------------------------------------------------

------------------------------------------------------------

------------------------------------------------------------

------------------------------------------------------------

------------------------------------------------------------

------------------------------------------------------------

------------------------------------------------------------

------------------------------------------------------------

------------------------------------------------------------

------------------------------------------------------------

## WHAT GOOD THINGS HAPPENED TODAY?

------------------------------------------------------------

------------------------------------------------------------

------------------------------------------------------------

## NOTE TO SELF...

If I could do anything different, I would...

------------------------------------------------------------

------------------------------------------------------------

------------------------------------------------------------

------------------------------------------------------------

23

## HEALTH & WELLNESS

FOOD

BREAKFAST:
_____

LUNCH:
_____

DINNER:
_____

SNACK (IF ANY):
_____

WATER INTAKE ▢▢▢▢▢▢▢▢

EXERCISE

(Description) _____

TIME:          QUALITY:          HRS:

OTHER

HRS OF TV, COMPUTER, PHONE:
_____

MEDS:                    ALCOHOL/DRUGS:
_____        _____

## HOW DID YOU SLEEP?

HRS OF SLEEP: _____     QUALITY OF SLEEP: ① ② ③ ④ ⑤ ⑥ ⑦ ⑧ ⑨ ⑩

HOW DID I MAKE MYSELF A PRIORITY TODAY?

-------------------------------------------

## LET'S TALK ABOUT IT. TODAY I AM...

**GRATEFUL FOR:**

-------------------------------------------

**FEELING (WHY? USE FEELING WORDS FROM LIST):**

○                    ○

○                    ○

**TALKED TO** (HOW DID I FEEL AFTER?):

-------------------------------------------

**LISTENING TO:**

-------------------------------------------

**READING:**

-------------------------------------------

## TODAY'S  REFLECTION

(EUSTRESSIN' OR YOU STRESSIN?)

---------------------------------------------------------------

---------------------------------------------------------------

---------------------------------------------------------------

---------------------------------------------------------------

---------------------------------------------------------------

---------------------------------------------------------------

---------------------------------------------------------------

---------------------------------------------------------------

---------------------------------------------------------------

## WHAT GOOD THINGS HAPPENED TODAY?

---------------------------------------------------------------

---------------------------------------------------------------

---------------------------------------------------------------

## NOTE TO SELF...

If I could do anything different, I would...

---------------------------------------------------------------

---------------------------------------------------------------

---------------------------------------------------------------

---------------------------------------------------------------

## HEALTH & WELLNESS

FOOD

☕ BREAKFAST:

_____

🥤 LUNCH:

_____

🍽 DINNER:

_____

▢ SNACK (IF ANY):

_____

WATER INTAKE  ▢▢▢▢▢▢▢▢

EXERCISE

(Description) _____

TIME:          QUALITY:          HRS:

OTHER

📺 HRS OF TV, COMPUTER, PHONE:

_____

MEDS: _____          ALCOHOL/DRUGS: _____

## HOW DID YOU SLEEP?

🕐 HRS OF SLEEP: _____          QUALITY OF SLEEP: ① ② ③ ④ ⑤ ⑥ ⑦ ⑧ ⑨ ⑩

HOW DID I MAKE MYSELF A PRIORITY TODAY?

-------------------------------------------------------------

## LET'S TALK ABOUT IT.  TODAY I AM...

**GRATEFUL FOR:**

-------------------------------------------------------------

**FEELING (WHY? USE FEELING WORDS FROM LIST):**

○                                              ○

○                                              ○

**TALKED TO** (HOW DID I FEEL AFTER?):

-------------------------------------------------------------

**LISTENING TO:**

-------------------------------------------------------------

**READING:**

-------------------------------------------------------------

## TODAY'S REFLECTION
(EUSTRESSIN' OR YOU STRESSIN?)

-------------------------------------------------------------------------
-------------------------------------------------------------------------
-------------------------------------------------------------------------
-------------------------------------------------------------------------
-------------------------------------------------------------------------
-------------------------------------------------------------------------
-------------------------------------------------------------------------
-------------------------------------------------------------------------
-------------------------------------------------------------------------
-------------------------------------------------------------------------

## WHAT GOOD THINGS HAPPENED TODAY?

-------------------------------------------------------------------------
-------------------------------------------------------------------------
-------------------------------------------------------------------------

## NOTE TO SELF...
If I could do anything different, I would...

-------------------------------------------------------------------------
-------------------------------------------------------------------------
-------------------------------------------------------------------------
-------------------------------------------------------------------------

## HEALTH & WELLNESS

FOOD

WATER INTAKE

🍵 BREAKFAST:

EXERCISE

(Description) _____

🥤 LUNCH:

TIME:          QUALITY:          HRS:

🍽 DINNER:

OTHER

📺 HRS OF TV, COMPUTER, PHONE:

▢ SNACK (IF ANY):

MEDS:                    ALCOHOL/DRUGS:

## HOW DID YOU SLEEP?

🕐 HRS OF SLEEP: _____        QUALITY OF SLEEP: ① ② ③ ④ ⑤ ⑥ ⑦ ⑧ ⑨ ⑩

HOW DID I MAKE MYSELF A PRIORITY TODAY?

-------------------------------------------------------------------

## LET'S TALK ABOUT IT.  TODAY I AM...

**GRATEFUL FOR:**

-------------------------------------------------------------------

**FEELING (WHY? USE FEELING WORDS FROM LIST):**

○                                    ○

○                                    ○

**TALKED TO** (HOW DID I FEEL AFTER?):

-------------------------------------------------------------------

**LISTENING TO:**

-------------------------------------------------------------------

**READING:**

-------------------------------------------------------------------

## TODAY'S REFLECTION
(EUSTRESSIN' OR YOU STRESSIN?)

-------------------------------------------------------------------

-------------------------------------------------------------------

-------------------------------------------------------------------

-------------------------------------------------------------------

-------------------------------------------------------------------

-------------------------------------------------------------------

-------------------------------------------------------------------

-------------------------------------------------------------------

-------------------------------------------------------------------

-------------------------------------------------------------------

## WHAT GOOD THINGS HAPPENED TODAY?

-------------------------------------------------------------------

-------------------------------------------------------------------

-------------------------------------------------------------------

## NOTE TO SELF...
If I could do anything different, I would...

-------------------------------------------------------------------

-------------------------------------------------------------------

-------------------------------------------------------------------

-------------------------------------------------------------------

# A WEEK IN REVIEW

## RATE YOUR OVERALL WEEK

( 1 )—( 2 )—( 3 )—( 4 )—( 5 )—( 6 )—( 7 )—( 8 )—( 9 )—( 10 )

NEEDS
WORK                        GOOD, BUT COULD USE IMPROVEMENT                        GREAT,
                                                                                  FULFILLING WEEK!

🕐 TOTAL HRS OF SLEEP: _____          💧 TOTAL WATER INTAKE: _____

🍴 TOTAL HEALTHY MEALS: _____         🏋 TOTAL HRS OF EXERCISE: _____

? DRUG/ALCOHOL INTAKE: _____          📺 TOTAL SCREEN TIME: _____

## ABOUT HOW MUCH ENERGY DID YOU PUT INTO POSITIVE THINKING?

|   |   |   |   |   |
|---|---|---|---|---|

0%          25%          50%          75%          100%

# ACCOMPLISHMENTS/ HIGHLIGHTS & INSIGHTS

- MY FAVORITE MOMENT THIS WEEK WAS...

--------------------------------------------------------------------

- THIS WEEK I LEARNED...

--------------------------------------------------------------------

- NEXT WEEK I'M GOING TO WORK ON...

--------------------------------------------------------------------

- AS I GO INTO NEXT WEEK, I FEEL...

--------------------------------------------------------------------

(Use this space as a rant sheet or as free space
to clear your mind/reflect on this week)

## HEALTH & WELLNESS

FOOD

🍵 BREAKFAST:

🥤 LUNCH:

🍽 DINNER:

▫ SNACK (IF ANY):

WATER INTAKE

EXERCISE

(Description) _____

TIME:         QUALITY:         HRS:

OTHER

📺 HRS OF TV, COMPUTER, PHONE:

MEDS:                ALCOHOL/DRUGS:

## HOW DID YOU SLEEP?

🕐 HRS OF SLEEP: _____     QUALITY OF SLEEP: ① ② ③ ④ ⑤ ⑥ ⑦ ⑧ ⑨ ⑩

HOW DID I MAKE MYSELF A PRIORITY TODAY?

## LET'S TALK ABOUT IT.  TODAY I AM...

**GRATEFUL FOR:**

**FEELING (WHY? USE FEELING WORDS FROM LIST):**

O                    O

O                    O

**TALKED TO** (HOW DID I FEEL AFTER?):

**LISTENING TO:**

**READING:**

## TODAY'S REFLECTION
(EUSTRESSIN' OR YOU STRESSIN?)

---------------------------------------------------------------

---------------------------------------------------------------

---------------------------------------------------------------

---------------------------------------------------------------

---------------------------------------------------------------

---------------------------------------------------------------

---------------------------------------------------------------

---------------------------------------------------------------

---------------------------------------------------------------

## WHAT GOOD THINGS HAPPENED TODAY?

---------------------------------------------------------------

---------------------------------------------------------------

---------------------------------------------------------------

## NOTE TO SELF...
If I could do anything different, I would...

---------------------------------------------------------------

---------------------------------------------------------------

---------------------------------------------------------------

---------------------------------------------------------------

## HEALTH & WELLNESS

FOOD

☕ BREAKFAST:

🥤 LUNCH:

🍲 DINNER:

🔲 SNACK (IF ANY):

WATER INTAKE 🥛🥛🥛🥛🥛🥛🥛🥛

EXERCISE

(Description) _____

TIME:          QUALITY:          HRS:

**OTHER**

📺 HRS OF TV, COMPUTER, PHONE:

MEDS:                    ALCOHOL/DRUGS:

## HOW DID YOU SLEEP?

🕐 HRS OF SLEEP: _____     **QUALITY OF SLEEP:** ① ② ③ ④ ⑤ ⑥ ⑦ ⑧ ⑨ ⑩

HOW DID I MAKE MYSELF A PRIORITY TODAY?

-------------------------------------------------------------------

## LET'S TALK ABOUT IT.  TODAY I AM...

**GRATEFUL FOR:**

-------------------------------------------------------------------

**FEELING (WHY? USE FEELING WORDS FROM LIST):**

○                                    ○

○                                    ○

**TALKED TO** (HOW DID I FEEL AFTER?):

-------------------------------------------------------------------

**LISTENING TO:**

-------------------------------------------------------------------

**READING:**

-------------------------------------------------------------------

## TODAY'S REFLECTION
(EUSTRESSIN' OR YOU STRESSIN?)

------------------------------------------------------------

------------------------------------------------------------

------------------------------------------------------------

------------------------------------------------------------

------------------------------------------------------------

------------------------------------------------------------

------------------------------------------------------------

------------------------------------------------------------

------------------------------------------------------------

------------------------------------------------------------

## WHAT GOOD THINGS HAPPENED TODAY?

------------------------------------------------------------

------------------------------------------------------------

------------------------------------------------------------

## NOTE TO SELF...
If I could do anything different, I would...

------------------------------------------------------------

------------------------------------------------------------

------------------------------------------------------------

## HEALTH & WELLNESS

FOOD

☕ BREAKFAST:

🥤 LUNCH:

🍽 DINNER:

☐ SNACK (IF ANY):

WATER INTAKE ▯▯▯▯▯▯▯▯

EXERCISE

(Description) _____

TIME:        QUALITY:        HRS:

OTHER

📺 HRS OF TV, COMPUTER, PHONE:

MEDS:                ALCOHOL/DRUGS:

## HOW DID YOU SLEEP?

🕐 HRS OF SLEEP: _____     QUALITY OF SLEEP: ① ② ③ ④ ⑤ ⑥ ⑦ ⑧ ⑨ ⑩

HOW DID I MAKE MYSELF A PRIORITY TODAY?

------------------------------------------------

## LET'S TALK ABOUT IT. TODAY I AM...

GRATEFUL FOR:

------------------------------------------------

FEELING (WHY? USE FEELING WORDS FROM LIST):

○                    ○

○                    ○

TALKED TO (HOW DID I FEEL AFTER?):

------------------------------------------------

LISTENING TO:

------------------------------------------------

READING:

------------------------------------------------

## TODAY'S REFLECTION

(EUSTRESSIN' OR YOU STRESSIN?)

-------------------------------------------------------------------------

-------------------------------------------------------------------------

-------------------------------------------------------------------------

-------------------------------------------------------------------------

-------------------------------------------------------------------------

-------------------------------------------------------------------------

-------------------------------------------------------------------------

-------------------------------------------------------------------------

-------------------------------------------------------------------------

-------------------------------------------------------------------------

## WHAT GOOD THINGS HAPPENED TODAY?

-------------------------------------------------------------------------

-------------------------------------------------------------------------

-------------------------------------------------------------------------

## NOTE TO SELF...

If I could do anything different, I would...

-------------------------------------------------------------------------

-------------------------------------------------------------------------

-------------------------------------------------------------------------

-------------------------------------------------------------------------

## HEALTH & WELLNESS

FOOD

☕ BREAKFAST:
_____

🥤 LUNCH:
_____

🍲 DINNER:
_____

▢ SNACK (IF ANY):
_____

WATER INTAKE 🥛🥛🥛🥛🥛🥛🥛🥛

EXERCISE

(Description) _____

TIME:          QUALITY:          HRS:

OTHER

📺 HRS OF TV, COMPUTER, PHONE:
_____

MEDS:                    ALCOHOL/DRUGS:
_____          _____

## HOW DID YOU SLEEP?

🕐 HRS OF SLEEP: _____     QUALITY OF SLEEP: ① ② ③ ④ ⑤ ⑥ ⑦ ⑧ ⑨ ⑩

HOW DID I MAKE MYSELF A PRIORITY TODAY?

--------------------------------------------------

## LET'S TALK ABOUT IT.  TODAY I AM...

GRATEFUL FOR:

--------------------------------------------------

FEELING (WHY? USE FEELING WORDS FROM LIST):

○                              ○

○                              ○

TALKED TO (HOW DID I FEEL AFTER?):

--------------------------------------------------

LISTENING TO:

--------------------------------------------------

READING:

--------------------------------------------------

## TODAY'S REFLECTION
(EUSTRESSIN' OR YOU STRESSIN?)

------------------------------------------------------------

------------------------------------------------------------

------------------------------------------------------------

------------------------------------------------------------

------------------------------------------------------------

------------------------------------------------------------

------------------------------------------------------------

------------------------------------------------------------

------------------------------------------------------------

## WHAT GOOD THINGS HAPPENED TODAY?

------------------------------------------------------------

------------------------------------------------------------

------------------------------------------------------------

## NOTE TO SELF...
If I could do anything different, I would...

------------------------------------------------------------

------------------------------------------------------------

------------------------------------------------------------

## HEALTH & WELLNESS

FOOD

BREAKFAST:

LUNCH:

DINNER:

SNACK (IF ANY):

WATER INTAKE

EXERCISE

(Description) _____

TIME:        QUALITY:        HRS:

OTHER

HRS OF TV, COMPUTER, PHONE:

MEDS:                ALCOHOL/DRUGS:

## HOW DID YOU SLEEP?

HRS OF SLEEP: _____   QUALITY OF SLEEP: ① ② ③ ④ ⑤ ⑥ ⑦ ⑧ ⑨ ⑩

HOW DID I MAKE MYSELF A PRIORITY TODAY?

--------------------------------------------------

## LET'S TALK ABOUT IT. TODAY I AM...

GRATEFUL FOR:

--------------------------------------------------

FEELING (WHY? USE FEELING WORDS FROM LIST):

O          O

O          O

TALKED TO (HOW DID I FEEL AFTER?):

--------------------------------------------------

LISTENING TO:

--------------------------------------------------

READING:

--------------------------------------------------

Today's Date: / / SUN MON TUES WED THURS FRI SAT

## TODAY'S REFLECTION

(EUSTRESSIN' OR YOU STRESSIN?)

-----------------------------------------------------------------------

-----------------------------------------------------------------------

-----------------------------------------------------------------------

-----------------------------------------------------------------------

-----------------------------------------------------------------------

-----------------------------------------------------------------------

-----------------------------------------------------------------------

-----------------------------------------------------------------------

-----------------------------------------------------------------------

## WHAT GOOD THINGS HAPPENED TODAY?

-----------------------------------------------------------------------

-----------------------------------------------------------------------

-----------------------------------------------------------------------

## NOTE TO SELF...

If I could do anything different, I would...

-----------------------------------------------------------------------

-----------------------------------------------------------------------

-----------------------------------------------------------------------

-----------------------------------------------------------------------

41

## HEALTH & WELLNESS

FOOD

☕ BREAKFAST:

🥤 LUNCH:

🍽 DINNER:

⬜ SNACK (IF ANY):

WATER INTAKE

EXERCISE

(Description) _____

TIME:        QUALITY:        HRS:

**OTHER**

📺 HRS OF TV, COMPUTER, PHONE:

MEDS:              ALCOHOL/DRUGS:

## HOW DID YOU SLEEP?

🕐 HRS OF SLEEP: _____    QUALITY OF SLEEP: ① ② ③ ④ ⑤ ⑥ ⑦ ⑧ ⑨ ⑩

HOW DID I MAKE MYSELF A PRIORITY TODAY?

---

## LET'S TALK ABOUT IT. TODAY I AM...

**GRATEFUL FOR:**

---

**FEELING (WHY? USE FEELING WORDS FROM LIST):**

○                          ○

○                          ○

**TALKED TO** (HOW DID I FEEL AFTER?):

---

**LISTENING TO:**

---

**READING:**

## TODAY'S REFLECTION
(EUSTRESSIN' OR YOU STRESSIN?)

----------------------------------------

----------------------------------------

----------------------------------------

----------------------------------------

----------------------------------------

----------------------------------------

----------------------------------------

----------------------------------------

----------------------------------------

## WHAT GOOD THINGS HAPPENED TODAY?

----------------------------------------

----------------------------------------

----------------------------------------

## NOTE TO SELF...
If I could do anything different, I would...

----------------------------------------

----------------------------------------

----------------------------------------

## HEALTH & WELLNESS

FOOD

☕ BREAKFAST:

🥤 LUNCH:

🍽 DINNER:

▢ SNACK (IF ANY):

WATER INTAKE ▯▯▯▯▯▯▯▯

EXERCISE

(Description) _____

TIME:     QUALITY:     HRS:

**OTHER**

📺 HRS OF TV, COMPUTER, PHONE:

MEDS:       ALCOHOL/DRUGS:

## HOW DID YOU SLEEP?

🕐 **HRS OF SLEEP:** _____    **QUALITY OF SLEEP:** ① ② ③ ④ ⑤ ⑥ ⑦ ⑧ ⑨ ⑩

HOW DID I MAKE MYSELF A PRIORITY TODAY?

- - - - - - - - - - - - - - - - - - - - - - - - - - - - - - - - - - - - - - - - - - - - - -

## LET'S TALK ABOUT IT. TODAY I AM...

**GRATEFUL FOR:**

- - - - - - - - - - - - - - - - - - - - - - - - - - - - - - - - - - - - - - - - - - - - - -

**FEELING (WHY? USE FEELING WORDS FROM LIST):**

○                ○

○                ○

**TALKED TO** (HOW DID I FEEL AFTER?):

- - - - - - - - - - - - - - - - - - - - - - - - - - - - - - - - - - - - - - - - - - - - - -

**LISTENING TO:**

- - - - - - - - - - - - - - - - - - - - - - - - - - - - - - - - - - - - - - - - - - - - - -

**READING:**

- - - - - - - - - - - - - - - - - - - - - - - - - - - - - - - - - - - - - - - - - - - - - -

## TODAY'S REFLECTION
(EUSTRESSIN' OR YOU STRESSIN?)

--------------------------------------------------------------------

--------------------------------------------------------------------

--------------------------------------------------------------------

--------------------------------------------------------------------

--------------------------------------------------------------------

--------------------------------------------------------------------

--------------------------------------------------------------------

--------------------------------------------------------------------

--------------------------------------------------------------------

--------------------------------------------------------------------

## WHAT GOOD THINGS HAPPENED TODAY?

--------------------------------------------------------------------

--------------------------------------------------------------------

--------------------------------------------------------------------

## NOTE TO SELF...
If I could do anything different, I would...

--------------------------------------------------------------------

--------------------------------------------------------------------

--------------------------------------------------------------------

--------------------------------------------------------------------

# A WEEK IN REVIEW

## RATE YOUR OVERALL WEEK

( 1 )—( 2 )—( 3 )—( 4 )—( 5 )—( 6 )—( 7 )—( 8 )—( 9 )—( 10 )

NEEDS
WORK

GOOD, BUT COULD USE IMPROVEMENT

GREAT,
FULFILLING WEEK!

🕐 TOTAL HRS OF SLEEP: _____

🍴 TOTAL HEALTHY MEALS: _____

? DRUG/ALCOHOL INTAKE: _____

💧 TOTAL WATER INTAKE: _____

TOTAL HRS OF EXERCISE: _____

📺 TOTAL SCREEN TIME: _____

## ABOUT HOW MUCH ENERGY DID YOU PUT INTO POSITIVE THINKING?

| | | | | |
|---|---|---|---|---|
| 0% | 25% | 50% | 75% | 100% |

# ACCOMPLISHMENTS/ HIGHLIGHTS & INSIGHTS

- MY FAVORITE MOMENT THIS WEEK WAS...

-------------------------------------------------------------------

- THIS WEEK I LEARNED...

-------------------------------------------------------------------

- NEXT WEEK I'M GOING TO WORK ON...

-------------------------------------------------------------------

- AS I GO INTO NEXT WEEK, I FEEL...

-------------------------------------------------------------------

(Use this space as a rant sheet or as free space
to clear your mind/reflect on this week)

## HEALTH & WELLNESS

FOOD

☕ BREAKFAST:

🥤 LUNCH:

🍽 DINNER:

▯ SNACK (IF ANY):

WATER INTAKE ▢▢▢▢▢▢▢▢

EXERCISE

(Description) _____

TIME:        QUALITY:        HRS:

OTHER

📺 HRS OF TV, COMPUTER, PHONE:

MEDS:              ALCOHOL/DRUGS:

## HOW DID YOU SLEEP?

🕐 HRS OF SLEEP: _____    QUALITY OF SLEEP: ① ② ③ ④ ⑤ ⑥ ⑦ ⑧ ⑨ ⑩

HOW DID I MAKE MYSELF A PRIORITY TODAY?

--------------------------------------------

## LET'S TALK ABOUT IT. TODAY I AM...

**GRATEFUL FOR:**

--------------------------------------------

**FEELING (WHY? USE FEELING WORDS FROM LIST):**

○                    ○

○                    ○

**TALKED TO** (HOW DID I FEEL AFTER?):

--------------------------------------------

**LISTENING TO:**

--------------------------------------------

**READING:**

--------------------------------------------

## TODAY'S REFLECTION

(EUSTRESSIN' OR YOU STRESSIN?)

-----------------------------------------------------------------

-----------------------------------------------------------------

-----------------------------------------------------------------

-----------------------------------------------------------------

-----------------------------------------------------------------

-----------------------------------------------------------------

-----------------------------------------------------------------

-----------------------------------------------------------------

-----------------------------------------------------------------

## WHAT GOOD THINGS HAPPENED TODAY?

-----------------------------------------------------------------

-----------------------------------------------------------------

-----------------------------------------------------------------

## NOTE TO SELF...

If I could do anything different, I would...

-----------------------------------------------------------------

-----------------------------------------------------------------

-----------------------------------------------------------------

## HEALTH & WELLNESS

FOOD

BREAKFAST:

LUNCH:

DINNER:

SNACK (IF ANY):

WATER INTAKE

EXERCISE

(Description) _____

TIME:          QUALITY:          HRS:

**OTHER**

HRS OF TV, COMPUTER, PHONE:

MEDS:                    ALCOHOL/DRUGS:

## HOW DID YOU SLEEP?

HRS OF SLEEP: _____     QUALITY OF SLEEP: ① ② ③ ④ ⑤ ⑥ ⑦ ⑧ ⑨ ⑩

HOW DID I MAKE MYSELF A PRIORITY TODAY?

----------------------------------------

## LET'S TALK ABOUT IT. TODAY I AM...

**GRATEFUL FOR:**

----------------------------------------

**FEELING (WHY? USE FEELING WORDS FROM LIST):**

○                              ○

○                              ○

**TALKED TO** (HOW DID I FEEL AFTER?):

----------------------------------------

**LISTENING TO:**

----------------------------------------

**READING:**

----------------------------------------

51

## TODAY'S  REFLECTION
(EUSTRESSIN' OR YOU STRESSIN?)

------------------------------------------------------------

------------------------------------------------------------

------------------------------------------------------------

------------------------------------------------------------

------------------------------------------------------------

------------------------------------------------------------

------------------------------------------------------------

------------------------------------------------------------

------------------------------------------------------------

## WHAT GOOD THINGS HAPPENED TODAY?

------------------------------------------------------------

------------------------------------------------------------

------------------------------------------------------------

## NOTE TO SELF...
If I could do anything different, I would...

------------------------------------------------------------

------------------------------------------------------------

------------------------------------------------------------

## HEALTH & WELLNESS

FOOD

BREAKFAST:

LUNCH:

DINNER:

SNACK (IF ANY):

WATER INTAKE

EXERCISE

(Description)

TIME:          QUALITY:          HRS:

OTHER

HRS OF TV, COMPUTER, PHONE:

MEDS:                    ALCOHOL/DRUGS:

## HOW DID YOU SLEEP?

HRS OF SLEEP: _____     QUALITY OF SLEEP: ① ② ③ ④ ⑤ ⑥ ⑦ ⑧ ⑨ ⑩

HOW DID I MAKE MYSELF A PRIORITY TODAY?

------------------------------------------------------------

## LET'S TALK ABOUT IT. TODAY I AM...

**GRATEFUL FOR:**

------------------------------------------------------------

**FEELING (WHY? USE FEELING WORDS FROM LIST):**

○                                        ○

○                                        ○

**TALKED TO** (HOW DID I FEEL AFTER?):

------------------------------------------------------------

**LISTENING TO:**

------------------------------------------------------------

**READING:**

------------------------------------------------------------

## TODAY'S REFLECTION
(EUSTRESSIN' OR YOU STRESSIN?)

---------------------------------------------------------------

---------------------------------------------------------------

---------------------------------------------------------------

---------------------------------------------------------------

---------------------------------------------------------------

---------------------------------------------------------------

---------------------------------------------------------------

---------------------------------------------------------------

---------------------------------------------------------------

## WHAT GOOD THINGS HAPPENED TODAY?

---------------------------------------------------------------

---------------------------------------------------------------

---------------------------------------------------------------

## NOTE TO SELF...
If I could do anything different, I would...

---------------------------------------------------------------

---------------------------------------------------------------

---------------------------------------------------------------

---------------------------------------------------------------

## HEALTH & WELLNESS

**FOOD**

☕ BREAKFAST:

🥤 LUNCH:

🍽 DINNER:

▭ SNACK (IF ANY):

**WATER INTAKE** 🥛🥛🥛🥛🥛🥛🥛🥛

**EXERCISE**

(Description) _____

TIME:          QUALITY:          HRS:

**OTHER**

📺 HRS OF TV, COMPUTER, PHONE:

MEDS:          ALCOHOL/DRUGS:

## HOW DID YOU SLEEP?

🕐 HRS OF SLEEP: _____     QUALITY OF SLEEP: ① ② ③ ④ ⑤ ⑥ ⑦ ⑧ ⑨ ⑩

HOW DID I MAKE MYSELF A PRIORITY TODAY?

--------------------------------------------------

## LET'S TALK ABOUT IT.  TODAY I AM...

**GRATEFUL FOR:**

--------------------------------------------------

**FEELING (WHY? USE FEELING WORDS FROM LIST):**

○                                    ○

○                                    ○

**TALKED TO** (HOW DID I FEEL AFTER?):

--------------------------------------------------

**LISTENING TO:**

--------------------------------------------------

**READING:**

--------------------------------------------------

54

## TODAY'S REFLECTION
(EUSTRESSIN' OR YOU STRESSIN?)

------------------------------------------------------------------------

------------------------------------------------------------------------

------------------------------------------------------------------------

------------------------------------------------------------------------

------------------------------------------------------------------------

------------------------------------------------------------------------

------------------------------------------------------------------------

------------------------------------------------------------------------

------------------------------------------------------------------------

------------------------------------------------------------------------

## WHAT GOOD THINGS HAPPENED TODAY?

------------------------------------------------------------------------

------------------------------------------------------------------------

------------------------------------------------------------------------

## NOTE TO SELF...
If I could do anything different, I would...

------------------------------------------------------------------------

------------------------------------------------------------------------

------------------------------------------------------------------------

------------------------------------------------------------------------

## HEALTH & WELLNESS

FOOD

☕ BREAKFAST:

🍎 LUNCH:

🍽 DINNER:

▫ SNACK (IF ANY):

WATER INTAKE  🥛🥛🥛🥛🥛🥛🥛🥛

EXERCISE

(Description) _____

TIME:          QUALITY:          HRS:

OTHER

📺 HRS OF TV, COMPUTER, PHONE:

MEDS:                    ALCOHOL/DRUGS:

## HOW DID YOU SLEEP?

🕐 HRS OF SLEEP: _____     QUALITY OF SLEEP: ① ② ③ ④ ⑤ ⑥ ⑦ ⑧ ⑨ ⑩

HOW DID I MAKE MYSELF A PRIORITY TODAY?

----------------------------------------

## LET'S TALK ABOUT IT. TODAY I AM...

**GRATEFUL FOR:**

----------------------------------------

**FEELING (WHY? USE FEELING WORDS FROM LIST):**

○                          ○

○                          ○

**TALKED TO** (HOW DID I FEEL AFTER?):

----------------------------------------

**LISTENING TO:**

----------------------------------------

**READING:**

----------------------------------------

## TODAY'S REFLECTION
(EUSTRESSIN' OR YOU STRESSIN?)

--------------------------------------------------------------

--------------------------------------------------------------

--------------------------------------------------------------

--------------------------------------------------------------

--------------------------------------------------------------

--------------------------------------------------------------

--------------------------------------------------------------

--------------------------------------------------------------

--------------------------------------------------------------

--------------------------------------------------------------

## WHAT GOOD THINGS HAPPENED TODAY?

--------------------------------------------------------------

--------------------------------------------------------------

--------------------------------------------------------------

## NOTE TO SELF...
If I could do anything different, I would...

--------------------------------------------------------------

--------------------------------------------------------------

--------------------------------------------------------------

--------------------------------------------------------------

## HEALTH & WELLNESS

FOOD

☕ BREAKFAST:

🥤 LUNCH:

🍽 DINNER:

▫ SNACK (IF ANY):

WATER INTAKE 🥛🥛🥛🥛🥛🥛🥛🥛

EXERCISE

(Description) _____

TIME:          QUALITY:          HRS:

OTHER

📺 HRS OF TV, COMPUTER, PHONE:

MEDS:                    ALCOHOL/DRUGS:

## HOW DID YOU SLEEP?

🕐 HRS OF SLEEP: \_\_\_\_\_     QUALITY OF SLEEP: ① ② ③ ④ ⑤ ⑥ ⑦ ⑧ ⑨ ⑩

HOW DID I MAKE MYSELF A PRIORITY TODAY?

## LET'S TALK ABOUT IT.  TODAY I AM...

**GRATEFUL FOR:**

**FEELING (WHY? USE FEELING WORDS FROM LIST):**

○                                    ○

○                                    ○

**TALKED TO** (HOW DID I FEEL AFTER?):

**LISTENING TO:**

**READING:**

## TODAY'S REFLECTION
(EUSTRESSIN' OR YOU STRESSIN?)

-----------------------------------------------------------------------

-----------------------------------------------------------------------

-----------------------------------------------------------------------

-----------------------------------------------------------------------

-----------------------------------------------------------------------

-----------------------------------------------------------------------

-----------------------------------------------------------------------

-----------------------------------------------------------------------

-----------------------------------------------------------------------

## WHAT GOOD THINGS HAPPENED TODAY?

-----------------------------------------------------------------------

-----------------------------------------------------------------------

-----------------------------------------------------------------------

## NOTE TO SELF...
If I could do anything different, I would...

-----------------------------------------------------------------------

-----------------------------------------------------------------------

-----------------------------------------------------------------------

## HEALTH & WELLNESS

FOOD

BREAKFAST:

_____

LUNCH:

_____

DINNER:

_____

SNACK (IF ANY):

_____

WATER INTAKE

EXERCISE

(Description) _____

TIME:          QUALITY:          HRS:

OTHER

HRS OF TV, COMPUTER, PHONE:

_____

MEDS: _____    ALCOHOL/DRUGS: _____

## HOW DID YOU SLEEP?

HRS OF SLEEP: _____     QUALITY OF SLEEP: ① ② ③ ④ ⑤ ⑥ ⑦ ⑧ ⑨ ⑩

HOW DID I MAKE MYSELF A PRIORITY TODAY?

-------------------------------------------------------------

## LET'S TALK ABOUT IT.  TODAY I AM...

**GRATEFUL FOR:**

-------------------------------------------------------------

**FEELING (WHY? USE FEELING WORDS FROM LIST):**

○                                    ○

○                                    ○

**TALKED TO** (HOW DID I FEEL AFTER?):

-------------------------------------------------------------

**LISTENING TO:**

-------------------------------------------------------------

**READING:**

-------------------------------------------------------------

## TODAY'S REFLECTION
(EUSTRESSIN' OR YOU STRESSIN?)

------------------------------------------------------------

------------------------------------------------------------

------------------------------------------------------------

------------------------------------------------------------

------------------------------------------------------------

------------------------------------------------------------

------------------------------------------------------------

------------------------------------------------------------

------------------------------------------------------------

------------------------------------------------------------

## WHAT GOOD THINGS HAPPENED TODAY?

------------------------------------------------------------

------------------------------------------------------------

------------------------------------------------------------

## NOTE TO SELF...
If I could do anything different, I would...

------------------------------------------------------------

------------------------------------------------------------

------------------------------------------------------------

------------------------------------------------------------

61

# A WEEK IN REVIEW

## RATE YOUR OVERALL WEEK

( 1 )—( 2 )—( 3 )—( 4 )—( 5 )—( 6 )—( 7 )—( 8 )—( 9 )—( 10 )

NEEDS
WORK                    GOOD, BUT COULD USE IMPROVEMENT                    GREAT,
                                                                        FULFILLING WEEK!

🕐 TOTAL HRS OF SLEEP: _____        💧 TOTAL WATER INTAKE: _____

🍴 TOTAL HEALTHY MEALS: _____        🏋 TOTAL HRS OF EXERCISE: _____

? DRUG/ALCOHOL INTAKE: _____        📺 TOTAL SCREEN TIME: _____

## ABOUT HOW MUCH ENERGY DID YOU PUT INTO POSITIVE THINKING?

| | | | | |
|---|---|---|---|---|
| | | | | |

  0%          25%          50%          75%          100%

# ACCOMPLISHMENTS/ HIGHLIGHTS & INSIGHTS

- MY FAVORITE MOMENT THIS WEEK WAS...

--------------------------------------------------------------------------------

- THIS WEEK I LEARNED...

--------------------------------------------------------------------------------

- NEXT WEEK I'M GOING TO WORK ON...

--------------------------------------------------------------------------------

- AS I GO INTO NEXT WEEK, I FEEL...

--------------------------------------------------------------------------------

(Use this space as a rant sheet or as free space
to clear your mind/reflect on this week)

## HEALTH & WELLNESS

FOOD

BREAKFAST:

_____

LUNCH:

_____

DINNER:

_____

SNACK (IF ANY):

_____

WATER INTAKE

EXERCISE

(Description) _____

TIME:          QUALITY:          HRS:

**OTHER**

HRS OF TV, COMPUTER, PHONE:

_____

MEDS:                    ALCOHOL/DRUGS:

_____        _____

## HOW DID YOU SLEEP?

🕐 HRS OF SLEEP: _____     **QUALITY OF SLEEP:** ① ② ③ ④ ⑤ ⑥ ⑦ ⑧ ⑨ ⑩

HOW DID I MAKE MYSELF A PRIORITY TODAY?

-------------------------------------------------------------------

## LET'S TALK ABOUT IT.  TODAY I AM...

**GRATEFUL FOR:**

-------------------------------------------------------------------

**FEELING (WHY? USE FEELING WORDS FROM LIST):**

○                                        ○

○                                        ○

**TALKED TO** (HOW DID I FEEL AFTER?):

-------------------------------------------------------------------

**LISTENING TO:**

-------------------------------------------------------------------

**READING:**

-------------------------------------------------------------------

## TODAY'S REFLECTION

(EUSTRESSIN' OR YOU STRESSIN?)

------------------------------------------------------------

------------------------------------------------------------

------------------------------------------------------------

------------------------------------------------------------

------------------------------------------------------------

------------------------------------------------------------

------------------------------------------------------------

------------------------------------------------------------

------------------------------------------------------------

------------------------------------------------------------

## WHAT GOOD THINGS HAPPENED TODAY?

------------------------------------------------------------

------------------------------------------------------------

------------------------------------------------------------

## NOTE TO SELF...

If I could do anything different, I would...

------------------------------------------------------------

------------------------------------------------------------

------------------------------------------------------------

------------------------------------------------------------

## HEALTH & WELLNESS

FOOD

☕ BREAKFAST:

_____

🥤 LUNCH:

_____

🍽 DINNER:

_____

▢ SNACK (IF ANY):

_____

WATER INTAKE ▯▯▯▯▯▯▯▯

EXERCISE

(Description) _____

TIME:          QUALITY:          HRS:

OTHER

📺 HRS OF TV, COMPUTER, PHONE:

_____

MEDS:                    ALCOHOL/DRUGS:

_____        _____

## HOW DID YOU SLEEP?

🕐 HRS OF SLEEP: _____     QUALITY OF SLEEP: ① ② ③ ④ ⑤ ⑥ ⑦ ⑧ ⑨ ⑩

HOW DID I MAKE MYSELF A PRIORITY TODAY?

-----------------------------------------------------------------

## LET'S TALK ABOUT IT. TODAY I AM...

**GRATEFUL FOR:**

-----------------------------------------------------------------

**FEELING (WHY? USE FEELING WORDS FROM LIST):**

○                                ○

○                                ○

**TALKED TO** (HOW DID I FEEL AFTER?):

-----------------------------------------------------------------

**LISTENING TO:**

-----------------------------------------------------------------

**READING:**

-----------------------------------------------------------------

## TODAY'S  REFLECTION
(EUSTRESSIN' OR YOU STRESSIN?)

-------------------------------------------------------------------

-------------------------------------------------------------------

-------------------------------------------------------------------

-------------------------------------------------------------------

-------------------------------------------------------------------

-------------------------------------------------------------------

-------------------------------------------------------------------

-------------------------------------------------------------------

-------------------------------------------------------------------

## WHAT GOOD THINGS HAPPENED TODAY?

-------------------------------------------------------------------

-------------------------------------------------------------------

-------------------------------------------------------------------

## NOTE TO SELF...
If I could do anything different, I would...

-------------------------------------------------------------------

-------------------------------------------------------------------

-------------------------------------------------------------------

-------------------------------------------------------------------

## HEALTH & WELLNESS

FOOD

☕ BREAKFAST:
_____

🥤 LUNCH:
_____

🍽 DINNER:
_____

▯ SNACK (IF ANY):
_____

WATER INTAKE ▭▭▭▭▭▭▭▭

EXERCISE

(Description) _____

TIME:          QUALITY:          HRS:

OTHER

📺 HRS OF TV, COMPUTER, PHONE:
_____

MEDS: _____     ALCOHOL/DRUGS: _____

## HOW DID YOU SLEEP?

🕐 HRS OF SLEEP: _____     QUALITY OF SLEEP: ① ② ③ ④ ⑤ ⑥ ⑦ ⑧ ⑨ ⑩

HOW DID I MAKE MYSELF A PRIORITY TODAY?
--------------------------------------------------

## LET'S TALK ABOUT IT.  TODAY I AM...

**GRATEFUL FOR:**
--------------------------------------------------

**FEELING (WHY? USE FEELING WORDS FROM LIST):**

○                              ○

○                              ○

**TALKED TO** (HOW DID I FEEL AFTER?):
--------------------------------------------------

**LISTENING TO:**
--------------------------------------------------

**READING:**
--------------------------------------------------

## TODAY'S REFLECTION
(EUSTRESSIN' OR YOU STRESSIN?)

-------------------------------------------------------------------

-------------------------------------------------------------------

-------------------------------------------------------------------

-------------------------------------------------------------------

-------------------------------------------------------------------

-------------------------------------------------------------------

-------------------------------------------------------------------

-------------------------------------------------------------------

-------------------------------------------------------------------

## WHAT GOOD THINGS HAPPENED TODAY?

-------------------------------------------------------------------

-------------------------------------------------------------------

-------------------------------------------------------------------

## NOTE TO SELF...
If I could do anything different, I would...

-------------------------------------------------------------------

-------------------------------------------------------------------

-------------------------------------------------------------------

-------------------------------------------------------------------

## HEALTH & WELLNESS

FOOD

☕ BREAKFAST:

_____

🥤 LUNCH:

_____

🍽 DINNER:

_____

▢ SNACK (IF ANY):

_____

WATER INTAKE  🥛🥛🥛🥛🥛🥛🥛🥛

EXERCISE

(Description) _____

TIME:          QUALITY:          HRS:

**OTHER**

📺 HRS OF TV, COMPUTER, PHONE:

_____

MEDS:                    ALCOHOL/DRUGS:

_____        _____

## HOW DID YOU SLEEP?

🕐 HRS OF SLEEP: _____     QUALITY OF SLEEP: ① ② ③ ④ ⑤ ⑥ ⑦ ⑧ ⑨ ⑩

HOW DID I MAKE MYSELF A PRIORITY TODAY?

--------------------------------------------------------------------

## LET'S TALK ABOUT IT.  TODAY I AM...

**GRATEFUL FOR:**

--------------------------------------------------------------------

**FEELING (WHY? USE FEELING WORDS FROM LIST):**

○                              ○

○                              ○

**TALKED TO** (HOW DID I FEEL AFTER?):

--------------------------------------------------------------------

**LISTENING TO:**

--------------------------------------------------------------------

**READING:**

--------------------------------------------------------------------

## TODAY'S REFLECTION
(EUSTRESSIN' OR YOU STRESSIN?)

---------------------------------------------------------------

---------------------------------------------------------------

---------------------------------------------------------------

---------------------------------------------------------------

---------------------------------------------------------------

---------------------------------------------------------------

---------------------------------------------------------------

---------------------------------------------------------------

---------------------------------------------------------------

## WHAT GOOD THINGS HAPPENED TODAY?

---------------------------------------------------------------

---------------------------------------------------------------

---------------------------------------------------------------

## NOTE TO SELF...
If I could do anything different, I would...

---------------------------------------------------------------

---------------------------------------------------------------

---------------------------------------------------------------

---------------------------------------------------------------

## HEALTH & WELLNESS

FOOD

☕ BREAKFAST:

_____

🥤 LUNCH:

_____

🍽 DINNER:

_____

▢ SNACK (IF ANY):

_____

WATER INTAKE  ⊔⊔⊔⊔⊔⊔⊔⊔

EXERCISE

(Description) _____

TIME:            QUALITY:            HRS:

**OTHER**

📺 HRS OF TV, COMPUTER, PHONE:

_____

MEDS:                    ALCOHOL/DRUGS:

_____        _____

## HOW DID YOU SLEEP?

🕐 HRS OF SLEEP: _____      QUALITY OF SLEEP: ① ② ③ ④ ⑤ ⑥ ⑦ ⑧ ⑨ ⑩

HOW DID I MAKE MYSELF A PRIORITY TODAY?

--------------------------------------------------------------------

## LET'S TALK ABOUT IT.  TODAY I AM...

**GRATEFUL FOR:**

--------------------------------------------------------------------

**FEELING (WHY? USE FEELING WORDS FROM LIST):**

○                                    ○

○                                    ○

**TALKED TO** (HOW DID I FEEL AFTER?):

--------------------------------------------------------------------

**LISTENING TO:**

--------------------------------------------------------------------

**READING:**

--------------------------------------------------------------------

## TODAY'S REFLECTION

(EUSTRESSIN' OR YOU STRESSIN?)

------------------------------------------------------------------

------------------------------------------------------------------

------------------------------------------------------------------

------------------------------------------------------------------

------------------------------------------------------------------

------------------------------------------------------------------

------------------------------------------------------------------

------------------------------------------------------------------

------------------------------------------------------------------

## WHAT GOOD THINGS HAPPENED TODAY?

------------------------------------------------------------------

------------------------------------------------------------------

------------------------------------------------------------------

## NOTE TO SELF...

If I could do anything different, I would...

------------------------------------------------------------------

------------------------------------------------------------------

------------------------------------------------------------------

------------------------------------------------------------------

## HEALTH & WELLNESS

FOOD

☕ BREAKFAST:

🥤 LUNCH:

🍽 DINNER:

▫ SNACK (IF ANY):

WATER INTAKE 🥛🥛🥛🥛🥛🥛🥛🥛

EXERCISE

(Description)

TIME:          QUALITY:          HRS:

**OTHER**

📺 HRS OF TV, COMPUTER, PHONE:

MEDS:                    ALCOHOL/DRUGS:

## HOW DID YOU SLEEP?

🕐 HRS OF SLEEP: _____     QUALITY OF SLEEP: ① ② ③ ④ ⑤ ⑥ ⑦ ⑧ ⑨ ⑩

HOW DID I MAKE MYSELF A PRIORITY TODAY?

-------------------------------------------------------------------

## LET'S TALK ABOUT IT.  TODAY I AM...

**GRATEFUL FOR:**

-------------------------------------------------------------------

**FEELING (WHY? USE FEELING WORDS FROM LIST):**

○                              ○

○                              ○

**TALKED TO** (HOW DID I FEEL AFTER?):

-------------------------------------------------------------------

**LISTENING TO:**

-------------------------------------------------------------------

**READING:**

## TODAY'S REFLECTION
(EUSTRESSIN' OR YOU STRESSIN?)

------------------------------------------------------------

------------------------------------------------------------

------------------------------------------------------------

------------------------------------------------------------

------------------------------------------------------------

------------------------------------------------------------

------------------------------------------------------------

------------------------------------------------------------

------------------------------------------------------------

------------------------------------------------------------

## WHAT GOOD THINGS HAPPENED TODAY?

------------------------------------------------------------

------------------------------------------------------------

------------------------------------------------------------

## NOTE TO SELF...
If I could do anything different, I would...

------------------------------------------------------------

------------------------------------------------------------

------------------------------------------------------------

------------------------------------------------------------

## HEALTH & WELLNESS

FOOD

WATER INTAKE ▽▽▽▽▽▽▽▽▽

☕ BREAKFAST:

EXERCISE

_____

(Description) _____

🥤 LUNCH:

TIME:          QUALITY:          HRS:

_____

**OTHER**

🍽 DINNER:

📺 HRS OF TV, COMPUTER, PHONE:

_____

_____

▢ SNACK (IF ANY):

MEDS:               ALCOHOL/DRUGS:

_____

_____        _____

## HOW DID YOU SLEEP?

🕐 **HRS OF SLEEP:** _____     **QUALITY OF SLEEP:** ① ② ③ ④ ⑤ ⑥ ⑦ ⑧ ⑨ ⑩

HOW DID I MAKE MYSELF A PRIORITY TODAY?

-------------------------------------------------------------

## LET'S TALK ABOUT IT.  TODAY I AM...

**GRATEFUL FOR:**

-------------------------------------------------------------

**FEELING (WHY? USE FEELING WORDS FROM LIST):**

○                                    ○

○                                    ○

**TALKED TO** (HOW DID I FEEL AFTER?):

-------------------------------------------------------------

**LISTENING TO:**

-------------------------------------------------------------

**READING:**

-------------------------------------------------------------

## TODAY'S REFLECTION
(EUSTRESSIN' OR YOU STRESSIN?)

------------------------------------------------------------

------------------------------------------------------------

------------------------------------------------------------

------------------------------------------------------------

------------------------------------------------------------

------------------------------------------------------------

------------------------------------------------------------

------------------------------------------------------------

------------------------------------------------------------

------------------------------------------------------------

## WHAT GOOD THINGS HAPPENED TODAY?

------------------------------------------------------------

------------------------------------------------------------

------------------------------------------------------------

## NOTE TO SELF...
If I could do anything different, I would...

------------------------------------------------------------

------------------------------------------------------------

------------------------------------------------------------

------------------------------------------------------------

# A WEEK IN REVIEW

**RATE YOUR OVERALL WEEK**

( 1 )—( 2 )—( 3 )—( 4 )—( 5 )—( 6 )—( 7 )—( 8 )—( 9 )—( 10 )

NEEDS
WORK

GOOD, BUT COULD USE IMPROVEMENT

GREAT,
FULFILLING WEEK!

🕐 **TOTAL HRS OF SLEEP:** _____

💧 **TOTAL WATER INTAKE:** _____

🍴 **TOTAL HEALTHY MEALS:** _____

⊪—⊪ **TOTAL HRS OF EXERCISE:** _____

? **DRUG/ALCOHOL INTAKE:** _____

📺 **TOTAL SCREEN TIME:** _____

## ABOUT HOW MUCH ENERGY DID YOU PUT INTO POSITIVE THINKING?

| | | | | |
|---|---|---|---|---|

0%        25%        50%        75%        100%

# ACCOMPLISHMENTS/ HIGHLIGHTS & INSIGHTS

• MY FAVORITE MOMENT THIS WEEK WAS...

-------------------------------------------------------------------

• THIS WEEK I LEARNED...

-------------------------------------------------------------------

• NEXT WEEK I'M GOING TO WORK ON...

-------------------------------------------------------------------

• AS I GO INTO NEXT WEEK, I FEEL...

-------------------------------------------------------------------

(Use this space as a rant sheet or as free space
to clear your mind/reflect on this week)

## HEALTH & WELLNESS

FOOD

☕ BREAKFAST:
_____

🥤 LUNCH:
_____

🍽 DINNER:
_____

▢ SNACK (IF ANY):
_____

WATER INTAKE  ▢▢▢▢▢▢▢▢

EXERCISE

(Description) _____

TIME:          QUALITY:          HRS:

**OTHER**

📺 HRS OF TV, COMPUTER, PHONE:
_____

MEDS:                          ALCOHOL/DRUGS:
_____          _____

## HOW DID YOU SLEEP?

🕐 HRS OF SLEEP: _____          QUALITY OF SLEEP: ① ② ③ ④ ⑤ ⑥ ⑦ ⑧ ⑨ ⑩

HOW DID I MAKE MYSELF A PRIORITY TODAY?

------------------------------------------------

## LET'S TALK ABOUT IT.  TODAY I AM...

**GRATEFUL FOR:**

------------------------------------------------

**FEELING (WHY? USE FEELING WORDS FROM LIST):**

○                                    ○

○                                    ○

**TALKED TO** (HOW DID I FEEL AFTER?):

------------------------------------------------

**LISTENING TO:**

------------------------------------------------

**READING:**

------------------------------------------------

## TODAY'S REFLECTION

(EUSTRESSIN' OR YOU STRESSIN?)

------------------------------------------------------------

------------------------------------------------------------

------------------------------------------------------------

------------------------------------------------------------

------------------------------------------------------------

------------------------------------------------------------

------------------------------------------------------------

------------------------------------------------------------

------------------------------------------------------------

## WHAT GOOD THINGS HAPPENED TODAY?

------------------------------------------------------------

------------------------------------------------------------

------------------------------------------------------------

## NOTE TO SELF...

If I could do anything different, I would...

------------------------------------------------------------

------------------------------------------------------------

------------------------------------------------------------

------------------------------------------------------------

## HEALTH & WELLNESS

FOOD

🍵 BREAKFAST:

_____

🥤 LUNCH:

_____

🍽 DINNER:

_____

⬜ SNACK (IF ANY):

_____

WATER INTAKE 🥛🥛🥛🥛🥛🥛🥛🥛

EXERCISE

(Description) _____

TIME:          QUALITY:          HRS:

**OTHER**

📺 HRS OF TV, COMPUTER, PHONE:

_____

MEDS:                ALCOHOL/DRUGS:

_____        _____

## HOW DID YOU SLEEP?

🕐 HRS OF SLEEP: \_\_\_\_\_    QUALITY OF SLEEP: ① ② ③ ④ ⑤ ⑥ ⑦ ⑧ ⑨ ⑩

HOW DID I MAKE MYSELF A PRIORITY TODAY?

_____

## LET'S TALK ABOUT IT. TODAY I AM...

**GRATEFUL FOR:**

_____

**FEELING (WHY? USE FEELING WORDS FROM LIST):**

○                    ○

○                    ○

**TALKED TO** (HOW DID I FEEL AFTER?):

_____

**LISTENING TO:**

_____

**READING:**

_____

## TODAY'S REFLECTION
(EUSTRESSIN' OR YOU STRESSIN?)

--------------------------------------------------------

--------------------------------------------------------

--------------------------------------------------------

--------------------------------------------------------

--------------------------------------------------------

--------------------------------------------------------

--------------------------------------------------------

--------------------------------------------------------

--------------------------------------------------------

## WHAT GOOD THINGS HAPPENED TODAY?

--------------------------------------------------------

--------------------------------------------------------

--------------------------------------------------------

## NOTE TO SELF...
If I could do anything different, I would...

--------------------------------------------------------

--------------------------------------------------------

--------------------------------------------------------

--------------------------------------------------------

## HEALTH & WELLNESS

FOOD

WATER INTAKE

☕ BREAKFAST:
_____

EXERCISE

(Description) _____

🥤 LUNCH:
_____

TIME:          QUALITY:          HRS:

🍽 DINNER:
_____

**OTHER**

📺 HRS OF TV, COMPUTER, PHONE:
_____

▢ SNACK (IF ANY):
_____

MEDS:                    ALCOHOL/DRUGS:
_____        _____

## HOW DID YOU SLEEP?

🕐 HRS OF SLEEP: _____     **QUALITY OF SLEEP:** ① ② ③ ④ ⑤ ⑥ ⑦ ⑧ ⑨ ⑩

HOW DID I MAKE MYSELF A PRIORITY TODAY?

------------------------------------------------

## LET'S TALK ABOUT IT.  TODAY I AM...

**GRATEFUL FOR:**

------------------------------------------------

**FEELING (WHY? USE FEELING WORDS FROM LIST):**

O                              O

O                              O

**TALKED TO** (HOW DID I FEEL AFTER?):

------------------------------------------------

**LISTENING TO:**

------------------------------------------------

**READING:**

------------------------------------------------

## TODAY'S REFLECTION
(EUSTRESSIN' OR YOU STRESSIN?)

------------------------------------------------------------------------

------------------------------------------------------------------------

------------------------------------------------------------------------

------------------------------------------------------------------------

------------------------------------------------------------------------

------------------------------------------------------------------------

------------------------------------------------------------------------

------------------------------------------------------------------------

------------------------------------------------------------------------

------------------------------------------------------------------------

## WHAT GOOD THINGS HAPPENED TODAY?

------------------------------------------------------------------------

------------------------------------------------------------------------

------------------------------------------------------------------------

## NOTE TO SELF...
If I could do anything different, I would...

------------------------------------------------------------------------

------------------------------------------------------------------------

------------------------------------------------------------------------

------------------------------------------------------------------------

# A WEEK IN REVIEW

**RATE YOUR OVERALL WEEK**

(1)—(2)—(3)—(4)—(5)—(6)—(7)—(8)—(9)—(10)

NEEDS WORK       GOOD, BUT COULD USE IMPROVEMENT       GREAT, FULFILLING WEEK!

🕐 **TOTAL HRS OF SLEEP:** _____      💧 TOTAL WATER INTAKE: _____

🍴 **TOTAL HEALTHY MEALS:** _____      TOTAL HRS OF EXERCISE: _____

? **DRUG/ALCOHOL INTAKE:** _____      📺 TOTAL SCREEN TIME: _____

## ABOUT HOW MUCH ENERGY DID YOU PUT INTO POSITIVE THINKING?

| | | | | |
|---|---|---|---|---|
| 0% | 25% | 50% | 75% | 100% |

# ACCOMPLISHMENTS/ HIGHLIGHTS & INSIGHTS

• MY FAVORITE MOMENT THIS WEEK WAS...

-------------------------------------------------------------------------

• THIS WEEK I LEARNED...

-------------------------------------------------------------------------

• NEXT WEEK I'M GOING TO WORK ON...

-------------------------------------------------------------------------

• AS I GO INTO NEXT WEEK, I FEEL...

-------------------------------------------------------------------------

(Use this space as a rant sheet or as free space
to clear your mind/reflect on this week)

# THIS MONTH IN *Review*

| WEEK 1 | |
|---|---|

| WEEK 2 | |
|---|---|

| WEEK 3 | |
|---|---|

| WEEK 4 – 5 | |
|---|---|

## *Monthly Totals*

| MY TOP FEELINGS FROM LIST | TOP THINGS I PRIORITIZED |
|---|---|
| | |

🕐 TOTAL HRS OF SLEEP: _____     💧 TOTAL WATER INTAKE: _____

🍴 TOTAL HEALTHY MEALS: _____     TOTAL HRS OF EXERCISE: _____

? DRUG/ALCOHOL INTAKE: _____     📺 TOTAL SCREEN TIME: _____

# SELF *Reflection*

I'M PROUD OF MYSELF BECAUSE...

THINGS I ACCOMPLISHED:

THINGS TO WORK ON:

HOW CAN I GROW FROM THIS MONTH'S CHALLENGES?

HOW CAN I USE WHAT I LEARNED THIS MONTH TO MAKE NEXT MONTH BETTER?

## RELAXING *Thoughts*

# HELPFUL *Resources*

**National Suicide Prevention Lifeline** 1-800-273-8255

**Crisis Text Line** Text HOME to 741741

**Website:** www.rwenshaun.com
**Eustress Inc.** www.EustressInc.org

**The Good Stress Company**
www.thegoodstresscompany.com

# Notes

# Notes

# Notes

# Notes

-------------------------------------------------------------

-------------------------------------------------------------

-------------------------------------------------------------

-------------------------------------------------------------

-------------------------------------------------------------

-------------------------------------------------------------

-------------------------------------------------------------

-------------------------------------------------------------

-------------------------------------------------------------

-------------------------------------------------------------

-------------------------------------------------------------

-------------------------------------------------------------

-------------------------------------------------------------

-------------------------------------------------------------

-------------------------------------------------------------

-------------------------------------------------------------

-------------------------------------------------------------

Made in the USA
Columbia, SC
18 December 2020